DISNEY'S

SIMBA

AND THE BIG FLOOD

GROLIER
BOOK CLUB EDITION

Once there was a young lion cub named
Simba. His best friends were Timon, a little
meerkat, and a big warthog called Pumbaa. The
thing they enjoyed doing most was . . . nothing!

One day after a big lunch of wiggly worms
and crunchy grubs, Simba's friends rested beside
the river.

Simba studied the clouds.

The cub scratched his head. "I think the cloud shapes mean something," he said. "I wish I could figure out what."

Timon yawned. "Why bother when there's so much sleeping to do?"

"Maybe clouds can tell you about the weather," said Pumbaa. "You know, whether it's going to rain or not."

"Do you think they can?" wondered Simba.

"What?" Timon looked up. "That's the silliest thing I've ever heard!"

The meerkat laughed and laughed. "You don't have to look at the clouds to know the weather."

"When you see the sun, it's a sunny day. Or just stick out your paw. If it gets wet, it's raining," Timon told them.

Pumbaa laughed, too. "You're probably right." Then the warthog decided to go for a swim.

"Are you sure, Timon?" Simba asked.

"Of course I am."
Timon stuck out his paw.
"You see? It isn't raining,"
he pointed out.
But just then, Pumbaa
jumped in the river.
SPLASH!

Timon was soaked.

Pumbaa called from the river, "Hey, Timon! Your paw is wet now. Is it raining?"

The warthog laughed so hard his big belly made the water ripple.

Simba laughed, too. But Timon didn't.

"I'm right," he insisted. "When your paw gets wet, then it's raining."

"Right," Pumbaa agreed. "So it must be raining now."

And Pumbaa and Simba laughed again.

The friends went to their sleeping spot.

"Nothing like a refreshing shower. Right, Timon?" Pumbaa asked. The meerkat didn't answer—he was still trying to dry off.

Simba stretched out on the sand. The sun warmed his fur. He yawned and said, "I can learn to understand clouds later." Then Simba fell asleep.

Before long, a young giraffe named Bahati
woke them up. "It's time to play," she called.

"Let's play slide 'n' bounce," said Pumbaa.

Timon and Simba took turns sliding down
Bahati's long neck and bouncing off Pumbaa
into the river.

Bahati said, "My mother is having a baby. Soon I'll have a little brother or sister."

"That's great!" Timon cried. "Then we'll have two slides!"

The friends had lots of fun. They didn't notice the black storm clouds filling the sky.

Suddenly it was as dark as night.
Thunder boomed! Lightning flashed!
"Yikes!" cried Pumbaa.
"Run for cover!" shouted Timon as rain
started pouring down from the sky.

The friends huddled
together.

Simba noticed the river
was rising higher and
higher. It was going
to flood!

"We must get to higher
ground," Simba told
the others.

The four friends ran for the hills.
They saw many other animals heading
the same way.

Bahati looked for her mother, but she
didn't see her.

The young giraffe
stopped running
and cried,
"What if
my mother
needs help?"
"Where could
she be?"
Simba asked.
"The last time
I saw her, she was
by the river,"
Bahati replied.

"Then let's go!" said Simba.

The storm was getting worse as the friends headed back to the river.

The wind almost bent the trees to the ground.

"Help! I'm a meer-kite!" wailed Timon as he hung onto Pumbaa's tail.

Suddenly a hippopotamus came running up to Bahati. "Your mother is trapped on an island farther up the river," the hippo cried. "The water is too high—no one can reach her!"

The four friends rushed off and soon found Bahati's mother, Sukari. The river raged all around the tiny island, making it impossible for her to escape.

"What can we do?" Bahati sobbed.

"We'll never be able to swim out there. We'd need fins!" shrieked Timon.

"Or wings," said Pumbaa.

But Simba had an idea.

"We can make a raft!"

The friends quickly
got to work.
     Bahati found some vines.
     Timon and Pumbaa
gathered fallen tree trunks.

Simba kept an
eye on the river.
It was rising fast.
They had to hurry!

Tying the trunks together was hard!
But by working together, the friends quickly
finished the raft.

They pushed the raft into the water. Simba and Bahati climbed aboard.

"Hang on!" Simba shouted as the raft bounced and dipped in the wild water.

Bahati cried, "Oh, no! We're going to float past the island!"

"There's only one thing to do," Simba said. He took one end of a vine between his teeth. The other end was tied to the raft. Then the small cub jumped into the water!

Simba swam to the island. His front paws
grabbed the sand. But the river pulled at
him. He started to slip!

Sukari quickly stretched down her long neck
and pulled Simba to safety.

Together they pulled the raft to the island.

Bahati and Sukari were happy to see each
other.
Soon both giraffes were on the raft.
Then Simba jumped on, too.

The little raft bounced on the water.

"All that bouncing is making me seasick,"
Timon said nervously.

Finally, the raft landed safely.

But their troubles weren't over.

"My baby is coming soon," Sukari said.

"There's a cave nearby," Timon offered. "You could go there."

The clouds were starting to clear. "I think it will stop raining soon," Simba said.

He was learning to understand clouds!

Bahati's mother went into the cave. The friends waited anxiously outside.

Other animals came to the cave. They wanted to welcome the new baby giraffe.

Simba felt terrible.

"It's all my fault," he said. "If I had learned to understand clouds sooner, I would have known the storm was coming. Then your mother would never have been trapped on the island."

"But it was your idea that saved my mother," Bahati said. "And you were so brave. Simba, you'll be a great lion one day."

"And you're already a great friend," Pumbaa told him. Timon nodded.

Just then the air was filled with an amazing sound as all the animals around the cave cheered for joy!

The friends found Sukari with her baby.

"Bahati, meet your brother," the mother giraffe said.

Bahati smiled. "Can he come out and play?"

Sukari laughed. "Not yet. He has to learn how to walk first."

Then Sukari turned to Simba. "You are a brave lion, Simba. Thank you for saving us."

The animals left so that
the mother and baby could rest.

"This calls for a celebration!"
Timon announced. "Grubs for
everyone!"

But Simba wasn't listening.
He was busy studying the sky.
"I have to watch the clouds to
make sure it isn't going to rain
again," he said.

"There isn't a cloud in the sky," Timon pointed out.

Simba looked up. His friend was right.

"Besides," continued Timon, "it's not going to rain. My paw isn't wet. See?"

Just then, Pumbaa jumped in the river. SPLASH!

"It looks like rain to me," joked Simba. Everyone except Timon started to laugh.

"What! Why . . ." Timon sputtered. Then he looked around at his laughing friends.

"I guess when it rains, it boars," said Timon with a shrug. "Hakuna matata."

Then they all laughed together.